A HORSE-AND-BUGGY DOCTOR
IN SOUTHERN INDIANA

A HORSE-AND-BUGGY DOCTOR IN SOUTHERN INDIANA

1825–1903

by Elisabeth Zulauf Kelemen

HISTORIC MADISON, INC.
Madison, Indiana 47250

COVER:
SKETCH OF DR. HUTCHINGS' OFFICE & HOSPITAL
BY NORMAN KOHLHEPP

DESIGNED BY JUDITH WORACEK BARRY
PRINTED IN THE UNITED STATES OF AMERICA
BY FINN TYPOGRAPHIC SERVICE, INC.

DISTRIBUTED BY
HISTORIC MADISON, INC.
301 W. FIRST STREET
MADISON, INDIANA 47250

CONTENTS

Mail-boat, City of Cincinnati, *on the Ohio.*

"WM. D. HUTCHINGS, M.D. & SURGEON"

In my childhood, the high point of any season was a visit to the home of my grandparents, Dr. and Mrs. William D. Hutchings, in Madison, Indiana. The spring wagon loaded with the trunks started off early from our home in Jeffersonville, some four hours down-river. Mother, my sister and I followed in the surrey, brakes screeching painfully as our old roan horse Rex, in the expert hands of my father, was manoeuvred down the steep levee and onto the ferry to Louisville, directly across the Ohio.

The regal mail-boat *City of Cincinnati,* wearing crowns on her two slender smokestacks, lay at the cobblestoned quay, still loading crates and boxes and serene, well-dressed passengers. Then the long narrow gangplanks were hoisted and she swung out into midstream with all the aplomb of an ocean liner. A mile or so up-river we passed our own house on the Indiana side and the maids waved white tablecloths from the roof of the porch. Dinner on the boat was lavish. The great table wore a little metal collar around the edge to keep the dishes from walking off. Everything clattered and tinkled in the exciting throb of the twin engines. A silver

I

The big house and doctor's dispensary, Madison, Indiana.

mushroom secured by a silver collar and slim chain corked the heavy glass water-bottle. Afterwards we were put down to rest on the narrow hard bunk in the narrow soap-smelling stateroom. The shutter was closed over the little window and, in spite of vociferous protests, we usually fell asleep.

At Madison, a cluster of Hutchings aunts stood on the dock. Another spring wagon awaited our baggage and my sister, who was "delicate," rode up with the driver, to my envy. The rest of us walked—I think it was up Broadway, though that seems somewhat out of the way. And when we passed the fountain—hoary then and neglected—I entered an enchanted world.

My grandfather moved his family from Vine Street to the "big house" at 120 West Third sometime in the early 1880's. The property ran through to Presbyterian Street, with stable and wagon shed at the back. It was a rambling patrician building of white brick. The stone lintel on the kitchen wing was carved with a worn date, the last digit illegible: 1840 or '48. The main house, said to have been built a few years later by the architect Francis Suire, had been the home of Jesse D. Bright, a U.S. Senator from Indiana who was expelled from the Senate for recognizing Jefferson Davis as President of the Confederate States. Later, it was occupied by Judge J. D. Cravens, who sold it to Dr. Hutchings.

Inside was a series of spacious rooms, each extending the width of the building and opening on a broad two-story wooden gallery on the garden side, shuttered against the weather—a wonderful place to play on rainy days. There was a cavernous cellar and a huge attic. A pony-size rocking horse that stood on the landing took me to untold foreign lands. In the attic, many things were put away and forgotten that furnish the core of the Memorial Museum today.

The small unpainted brick house that stood across the brick areaway constituted the doctor's office and dispensary. It is considerably older than the dwelling and had served as a law office before the doctor bought it. A letter from Grandmother to her elder daughters, at school in Cincinnati, tells of the change:

June 2, 1882

Dear Children:

Just received Maude's letter stating that you will be home Wednesday. This will be the last letter I send to 95 Park Avenue. I send you this clipped from the "Star," it explains itself. Bring it home with you as I want to keep it. I was foolish enough to feel real bad because you found out about the change which I wanted to be a complete surprise. Your father's office being changed will gain us more room and Papa will not be annoyed with the crying of children. Papa says you may have new furniture for the Parlor and Curtains, which I will wait until you come home to select. We intended to build this summer, make the back building two-story but gave it up for the present. You will receive by this mail a chk for $40.00 and Miss N. bill for $23.50 for sheet music which your Papa says pay and bring home receipt. Then if you have enough money to get a Piano Cover select one and bring home. I hope you will have enough to buy a large-print edition of Shakespeare that your Papa wishes and if the money holds out the books, at Second-hand store all of them (Shakespeare also). Mr. Ham talked of "Frank," "Desert Home" "Little Women" . . .

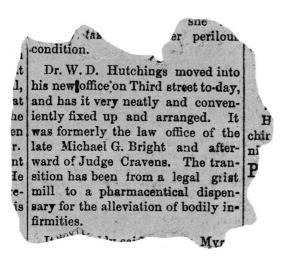

Clipping from the Madison Star, 1882.

The eldest daughter Maude wrote back to her favorite teacher in Cincinnati: "We have a new and lovely home. Our upper porch is splendid for viewing the beautiful sunsets. . . ."

As regards the separate office building, family tradition has it that the doctor was continuously bringing patients into the big house who were either too ill to be permitted to return to their homes or whose homes were inadequate for their care, and that Grandmother complained that her children were catching too many of the various ailments they brought in. The two large rooms downstairs in the office served as waiting-room and "surgery" and the two corresponding ones upstairs, as a sort of doctor's hospital. (The King's Daughters' Hospital was not established until 1899, my grandmother and her eldest daughter Maude being founding members. Maude refused nomination as Leader of the Hospital Circle, but was put on the Board of Managers.)

My own memories of my grandfather are vague. I have the impression of a rather stern personality whose word was law. He vaccinated me for smallpox when I was three. I remember that he was sitting in the front room of the Office, by a little table. He grasped me firmly by the upper arm and began scratching at the skin with a little knife. I protested and when he persisted I twisted round and kicked him. I remember him laughing softly—which at the time only added to my rage and frustration. He died the following year. His history comes down to me only through family traditions and the material that was preserved in the big house and was revealed when that was sold and the attic cleared for new tenants in 1938.

William Davies Hutchings was born on September 15th, 1825, at Lexington, Kentucky. (He died April 2, 1903, in Madison, Indiana.) In mid-18th century a Hutchings ancestor had set sail from Scotland for Boston with his two motherless sons, William and Oscar. He became ill and died on shipboard and was buried at sea. The ship's captain undertook to place the two orphaned boys; William was apprenticed to a confectioner, Oscar elsewhere. Neither was happy—who knows the details of such a life in 18th century New England? Oscar soon ran away, but William persisted and served out his apprenticeship. He took part in the Revolutionary War and apparently took out land as his soldier's bounty and moved to Kentucky. No intermediate family records have been discovered.

My grandfather, who bore his father's and grandfather's name, was probably the first-born son. The Hutchings home was close to Ashland, Henry Clay's mansion, and frequent visits there were among young William's earliest memories. Later, the family moved to Louisville. There was an older sister, Agnes, who died early, and at least one brother, Homer. A poem by Agnes was published in a Louisville newspaper in 1845. In a letter dated September 12, 1864, Homer wrote that he had sent "the couch" from Lexington via Adams Express. According to family tradition, this was part of a belated wedding gift—allegedly of Homer's own manufacture—a charming rosewood rocker and a loveseat, elaborately buttoned in black horsehair, which are still in family possession. There is no further mention of Homer in any letters. From later remarks, it must be assumed that the doctor lost most of his family at a comparatively early age.

From the age of six, William wished to be a doctor. In his library is a book on general medicine published in 1842, apparently purchased shortly after it appeared. While still in his teens, he "read" medicine with Dr. David McClure of Scott County (Indiana) for a year, then returned to Kentucky to study at the Academy in Lexington, where he graduated with the last class taught by the distinguished surgeon Benjamin Dudley.

At this time (1849), the settlements at the mouth of the Kentucky River were struck with Asiatic cholera, perhaps the worst epidemic the region ever suffered. Rich and poor alike went down. The weather was oppressively hot. The city of Lexington placed 100 cannon, obtained from the U.S. Artillery, in a circle around the town, firing a salvo every fifteen minutes every night, in hope of clearing the air.

With other youthful medicos from the Academy, William worked among the victims of the plague. Having noticed that the epidemic raged as long as the weather remained heavily overcast, muggy and windless, and that after a terrific thunderstorm with high winds no new cases developed and the sick began to convalesce, he pondered whether the electricity of the storm had dispelled the disease. At his graduation with highest honors from Asbury University of Indianapolis, in 1851, he took first prize for his thesis on the disease.

The efficacy and importance of electricity remained one of his hobbies. Convinced that its progress would revolutionize life, he made a note that he felt his best on a river trip, "because of the increased electricity in the air. . . ." For some types of therapy, he bought a complicated electrical "rejuvenator" which is part of the museum collection. And in 1887, he wrote to his eldest son, Fred, who had just obtained a promising position as an electrical engineer: "Electricity is the coming wonder of the world, now in its infancy, but destined to surmount every difficulty that stays our progress."

Diplomas are at hand from the Indiana Central Medical College of Indianapolis, class of 1851—a department of Asbury University (now DePauw) at Greencastle, Ind., that was in existence between 1850 and 1854; also an honorary degree from the College of Medicine of Ohio "in Doctoris in Medicina Gradua," 1873.

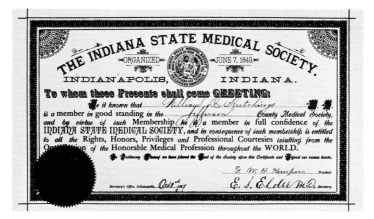

Some diplomas.

There are, as well, certificates from the Indiana State Medical Society, of his "good standing in the Jefferson County Medical Society," dated October 3, 1887, and his physician's license as of July 15, 1897, to the effect that "W. D. Hutchings has complied with the laws of the State of Indiana relating to the practice of Medicine, surgery, and obstetrics in the County and State aforesaid."

An idea of the cost of a medical education can be had from a letter from his brother-in-law Robert Koehler, whom Dr. Hutchings helped put through a course at Ann Arbor:

March 4, 1866

Dear Doctor—

I received yesterday by express fifty dollars from you and was exceedingly glad to get it as I had been out of funds . . . I will have sufficient now to see me to the close of the term which will be two weeks from now. I had hoped at the beginning of the session to go through for about $175. but my expenses at the college exceeded my anticipation. For matriculation and incidental expenses I paid $25., for dissecting $15.00, for "Ford's Quiz" and skelleton $9.00 making $49. and my traveling expenses will be $35., making $84.—leaving me $116. My board and lodging and lights cost me $4. a week—making just one hundred dollars. With the next two weeks you can see that I economized very well. . . .

Business at the University goes on as usual—only as is generally the case toward the close, there is not so much energy on the part of the faculty and most of the students as in the earlier part of the session. . . . Professor Gunn is still as interesting as ever in his department of Surgery—and our clinics are very good indeed. I wish you could see him, you would like him I know. He demonstrates all fractures, dislocations, etc. on a dead subject. And has been ligating all the artieries on a subject. He is now lecturing on the eye . . .

As a young doctor, William Hutchings practiced in Wooster, Scott County, Ind., in Johnson Township, near the Jefferson County line. Possibly he started practice in conjunction with a Dr. Woollen, an older man who is mentioned cordially in a number of family letters and remained a lifelong friend. The title of this chapter is quoted from his early signboard.

"Woostertown," always a tiny settlement, has long disappeared from the map. One wonders how and where the doctor lived, serving quite a stretch of the countryside. He drove a beautiful buggy—a status symbol in those days. The town bully, who had already run one young physician out of town, seared one of its varnished red wheels with a hot poker, and Dr. Hutchings's usually carefully restrained temper flared. He laid his gloves, handkerchief and wallet in his hat beside the medicine bag, leaped out and fell on the man, beating the fellow's head on the ground. He confessed later that if he had not been pulled off by bystanders, he feared he might have killed him. From that time, the new doctor went unmolested.

Family tradition has it that at one period of his life, the doctor spent some time abroad. It must have been during the 50's, when he was without ties. Regular steamship traffic already plied between the two continents, the engines assisted by the use of sails. A note in Maude's handwriting states that three rare books in his library, bound in leather and printed in London, were brought home from abroad. The range of subject is rather wide: "A Theoretical and chiefly Practical Treatise of Fevors, from the Latin of Gideon Harvey M.D." bears the date 1694. There are also "The Royal Gauger—as practised by the Officers of his Majesty's Revenue of Excise" (1776) and a new complete edition of Aristotle (1813), as well as French-Spanish and German-Italian dictionaries.

Otherwise, no proof of a trip was to be found—no letters nor souvenirs—until the discovery of a small packet of eight cards, which seemed to corroborate it. Two cards from Glasgow give a "seamen and emigrants' outfitting" firm and the address of a decorator and designer, apparently a personal friend. (Glasgow and Edinburgh hospitals were already famous at that time.) Another card names a private lodging house in London, another a coffee and chop house in St. Luke's, with various personal names and addresses on the back and the price of a lodging at 4s per night. (Two St. Luke's hospitals, well over a hundred years old, still function in London—one in Bayswater and the other in Chelsea.) Inter-

Souvenirs from a trip abroad.

esting is the card of an optical, mathematical and photographic instrument shop, recipient of honorable mention at an industrial exhibition in 1851.

That the doctor also visited the continent can be seen from the card of the Hotel London at Havre, in French and English, whose "omnibus leaves the hotel for every train." The owner's name is M. Hewlett. From Paris, a card of the Hotel des Étrangers, proprietor E. Krauth, boasts in English, French and Spanish that it is in the best section of Paris [near the Madeleine and the Opera] and offers every English comfort. On the back of this, the doctor wrote: "This is conveniently located & they speak English & the charges are moderate, would recommend it. Always make an agreement as to price before taking lodgement." He noted also the address of a *maison meublée*, 36 rue de Colisée—suggesting plans for a longer stay. Another card names a watchmaker who offers a guarantee with his products. It could not be established whether the doctor traveled as an interested tourist or was able to spend some time at the various medical centers.

It was in Wooster that Dr. Hutchings met his future wife. Matilda Christine Koehler was 15 years his junior, born on April 25, 1840, in Springfield, Ohio. (She died in Madison, February 13, 1914.) Her grandfather, also a doctor, had migrated with his family from the Kingdom of Württemberg (Germany), landing in Baltimore in 1819, according to her father's memoirs of the journey, which he took when he was a 14-year-old boy. The Koehler family soon scattered. With the drift toward the West, one son went as far as Texas, where he died, leaving 9000 acres of land unclaimed by heirs. Matilda's father, Herman Adolar Koehler (1805–1882), lived for a time in Springfield, Ohio, and married Aurore Gerhardine Ludeling (1814–1890), the daughter of a Bremen merchant who had settled near New Orleans. Restless, not too successful as farmer and storekeeper, Adolar drifted with his growing family into Southern Indiana.

In her mid-teens Matilda—or Tillie, as she was called—attended the Frederick Female Seminary, in Frederick, Maryland,

Matilda C. Koehler's report card, 1855.

living with an uncle there. Back home at the age of 17, she opened a school with an older sister. The handwritten contract reads:

> *This article of agreement made and entered into this day of December/57 between Mary Van Pelt and Matilda Koehler of the first part and the undersigned subscribers of the second part, witnesseth—*
> *The parties of the first part agree to teach a school in the town*

of Wooster one quarter or thirteen weeks and teach the following branches

Reading, Writing, Authography. Geography, Arithmetic, English-Grammar, Philosophy, dictionary, exercises in Catechism, History and Composition. They agree to teach in the school house and furnish their own fuel.

The parties of the second part agree to pay two dollars per quarter to each scholar, they (the scholars) conforming to all the rules of the school. And the subscribers will furnish all that is necessary for their children.

Any scholar who cannot by kind treatment be induced to conform to the rules of the school will be reported to their parents or Guardians after which if they continue refractory expelled the school and held liable for the tuition.

Matilda at the age of 17.
DAGUERREOTYPE.

Seventeen children are registered.

It should be realized that in mid-1800's, Ohio, Kentucky and Indiana were Far West. A woman's only possible employments were teaching and sewing or millinery. The Female Medical College opened in Philadelphia in 1850; Vassar College was founded in 1865; a professional school for nurses, in 1873.

A daguerreotype of Matilda at around 17 shows a radiant, romantic, impulsive girl. She and a friend must have sent Dr. Hutchings some apples in token of admiration. His carefully dignified reply is at hand on one of those bits of blue paper so characteristic of the "notes" of that day, folded to the size of a commemorative postage stamp, and addressed to Tillie and Celia:

Young Ladies

I accept with many thanks your agreeable present. You must have wandered into the gardens of Pomona in your romantic "ramble" and had the assistance of the goddess herself in gathering the ripe and blushing fruits with which you have complimented me. Flora too must have contributed to the offering as emblematic of olden times when the goddesses and Nymphs were in sweet communion.

With profound sentiments of regards, believe me

Your
Will.

The classical reference as well as the handwriting identify him. He liked to append an apt Latin motto to his medical articles and his infrequent but cogent letters to newspapers. His oldest daughter reports that when he was old and ill, he could recall only the Latin names of his drugs.

Tillie must have confessed a youthful crush on the doctor to her brother Herman, five years her senior, for he replied from his home in Maryland in a letter full of admonition: What made her believe that this experienced and older man should regard her with more interest than any of the other young ladies of the community? Was she careful that her behavior was not so forward as to lose his respect? Was she so uncertain about the situation that she should turn to him, her brother, so far away, instead of to her own dear, loving and understanding mother right at home?

Whatever the answers, Matilda C. Koehler and William D. Hutchings were married in the Fall of 1861, and shortly after moved to Lexington, Ind., some 18 miles southwest of Madison. Life during the Civil War was far from easy, even in such a small community. The churches were split into factions over the War. Tillie reports so much illness that the doctor was away many nights, though ill himself. "Here we are perfectly *mud-bound*. The buggy could not come when it was so bad and when the weather was fine, the doctor had no time.

"I am miserably lonely tonight, for Doctor is in Indianapolis at a convention (he is a delegate). Since he is gone they have been

Dr. William D. Hutchings and Matilda, his bride, 1861.
DAGUERREOTYPES.

coming for him. I have a list of names and the cry of each is 'Please tell him to come *as soon* as he is home'. Doctor had Charlie C. to come up at night, so I am not alone. You should see the desperate weapons ranged beside my bed for any emergency—make ready, aim, fire!'"

Dr. Hutchings had been reared as a Henry Clay Whig and acted with that party until its collapse; but when a sectional party arose on its ruins, he became affiliated with the American ("Know-nothing") party, in the vain effort among Southern Unionists to avoid civil war. At a meeting of the party in Wooster, June 28, 1856, he presented a set of resolutions which were unanimously adopted: "WHEREAS, If the proposition is true that the greatest evil short of annihilation, that can befall the American people, is a dissolution of the union of these States. . . then it behooves us as patriots and good citizens, to stand aloof from and set the seal of condemnation upon, any and every clique or sectional party, whose principles are calculated to bring such a horrible calamity upon us. . . . *Resolved*, 1st. That we are 'freemen', not of the North or of the South, but of the United States. . . . *Resolved*, 2nd. That the nomination of Fillmore and Donelson meets our unified approbation. . . ."

On the dissolution of the party, in 1860, the doctor became a National Democrat, always a staunch Union man, and grew so influential in Scott County "as to render it permanently Democratic." He was twice elected joint representative to the Indiana General Assembly for Scott, Jefferson, and Clark counties. At the time of Matilda's letter above, however, he refused nomination because of ill health and the pressure of his practice.

Letters show many visits to and from family members—at Christmas time, or when a new baby was expected, or when help was needed in case of illness. Tillie's two younger sisters, Aurora and Septima, often lived for months with the Hutchings. On the occasion of an early visit to the new home in Lexington, "Seppie" writes:

On Saturday a young lady gave me a hint that the Band was going to give Mrs. Hutchings and her sister a serenade tonight. . . . Dr. and

Robert had just gone to bed and Matilda was in the kitchen with Nancy (the hired girl) who was ironing, and I sitting in the rocking chair half asleep when we heard the low sound of instruments tuning. It was a string band. They played four or five tunes, we tossed them our cards, and they left, and we went to bed. . . .

Tillie speaks of riding the 24 miles to her parents in Manville, where they were established for a time after one of their many moves. Other means of transportation were by hack, stagecoach, rockaway (a form of surrey). Letters often went "by Bearer," hastily scribbled when it was discovered that some acquaintance was going into "town."

As the war continued, the doctor sold his much-prized buggy. Tradition has it that when Morgan's raiders passed through Lexington (1863), Matilda led his only horse into the tall corn and hid there until all was safe. (The action is perfectly credible to those who know how thick and high fodder corn grows in Indiana.)

Prices were rising steadily. They seem to have varied greatly with the locality. From Adolar Koehler's list of purchases for his store:

in 1862, Java coffee was 40¢ per pound
   coal oil . . . 60¢ a gallon, retailing at 75.
in 1863, sugar by the half-barrel, 120 lbs at 13⅓¢ wholesale
   flour . . . $7.50 per barrel, wholesale
   tea . . . 1.35 per pound
   beef . . . 15¢
   butter . . . 30¢
   brown sugar . . . 15¢, white . . . 19¢
by 1864, coffee had risen to 55¢ at a bargain, retailing in Madison at 65–
   68¢ a pound, and sugar was 27¢.

(Herman Koehler in Maryland wrote his mother at North Frankfurt, Ind., that, all other business enterprises having fallen through, he would remain in milk delivery for the time being—buying at 16¢ a gallon and selling at 24¢ in the winter and 20¢ in the summer. He later became a sutler for the United States Army.)

Madison, Indiana, from the Kentucky shore, 1893.

In 1869 Matilda wrote to Seppie: "Our RR almost completed. The Irishmen thick about town and business is brisk, particularly in the whiskey trade." By 1870, "cars are running past our town at last and in the Spring regular trains will run, though the depot here is not yet built." The railroad from Madison to Indianapolis was one of the earliest to be built west of the Alleghenies. From a dead-end station at the edge of town, the Jeffersonville, Madison & Indianapolis line ran north through the famous "cut"—a wonder of railroad engineering, so steep that a giant engine was needed to make the grade. In my day, the rails crossed those of the east-west line of the Baltimore & Ohio at North Vernon, some 22 miles or so north of Madison. But the schedules were not coordinated. We could come up the Ohio from Louisville by boat in four comfortable, even enjoyable hours; but by train, we had to wait four hours in the musty North Vernon station to make a connection.

Dr. Hutchings was appointed U.S. Examining Surgeon around 1867, but resigned two years later when he was re-elected to the Legislature. His service as representative accounts in part for the many law volumes in his library. He was again appointed U.S. Surgeon in 1885, as well as to the posts of Examining Physician for several insurance companies. He is mentioned as a Master Mason in 1868. In 1876, already with six children, the family moved from Lexington to a house on Vine Street in Madison — which was still a thriving river port, though its greatest prosperity had passed with the War. From there, six years later, they moved into the big white house that I knew as a child. Maude, Josephine, Willie (d. 1875), Charles Frederick, Robert, Herman, and Agnes (my mother) were born in Lexington; Lida and Zoe, in the late 70's in Madison. All are pictured in the chapter, "Family Album."

In 1967, at the request of my only surviving aunt, Lida Hutchings, my husband and I went to Madison to sort through the ma-

Family picture for the doctor's 6oth birthday, 1885.
DAGUERREOTYPE.

terial which she had stored in the Office. The first sight threw us into despair. The four ample rooms were literally piled to the ceiling with heterogeneous trunks, boxes, cartons, newspaper packages. Fortunately, most had been labeled — a gargantuan task in itself — when they were moved from the attic of the "big house." Resolving to keep only the early documents up to 1905, unless later ones were of primary importance, we cleared out some five pickup truckloads of miscellaneous trash — old coffee cans, paper bags, varying lengths of string, inconsequential letters, Christmas cards and invitations, newspapers, rags. We were just wishing to put the whole thing to the torch, when Mr. John Windle, President of Historic Madison, appeared at the door to see us, smudged as we were with coal dust that had sifted unheeded for years through a broken windowpane. He told us that he had long been interested in the house — closed, enigmatic, dilapidated — for Historic Madison, since, small as it is, it is one of the purest Greek Revival style buildings in the city. So, the plan for the memorial museum developed, to the great satisfaction of the last Hutchings daughter, 90 years old and far from her childhood home.

The compact red brick building that comprised the doctor's office and hospital, with its elegant pediment and the inner staircase ingeniously enclosed between masonry dividing walls, is indeed an early Greek Revival gem from around the 1830's: The little "skirt" below the eaves, the unobtrusive dentilation of the cornice at the sides, the stone lintels of the façade, all add dignity and elegance to the exterior. Norman Kohlhepp of Louisville, the artist of the cover sketch, wrote: "I want to tell you I was very impressed with the beauty of its proportions. . . . I measured the spaces and found five equal verticals . . . came home and found Jefferson's original 'Parthenon' rotunda [at the University of Virginia] has five equal spaces — it's beautiful!"

Enough remains to give an impression of the furnishings and equipment of Dr. Hutchings's office and dispensary. His rolltop desk and bookcase is there, along with the horsehair sofa and armchairs in the waiting room, decorations for the mantle piece, vases and lamps on the marble-topped tables, and the Seth Thomas calendar clock which Tillie proudly mentions acquiring in 1867. In one of the upstairs bedrooms is a large Victorian bed with carved headboard, in the other a much earlier piece which might have come down in the family or been acquired by the doctor with the property. This is a three-quarter-size bed, which has turned, low posts with mushroom caps, and spindles across the headboard. There is also a corner cupboard that might be an heirloom from the 18th century and a wig dresser in early French Empire manner—perhaps inherited from Tillie's Louisiana-born mother. Rare old quilts survive as coverlets. A cradle is there, and many bookcases filled with contemporary books, both scientific works and belles-lettres. Numerous engravings and family photographs grace the walls—with several portraits. One represents Tillie's favorite older brother Herman Koehler, an excellent amateur artist, who painted the fine watercolor landscapes that hang in the house.

Unusual and curious are two floral wreaths elaborately woven of human hair and enclosed in shadow boxes—funereal mementos of dear departed ones. They often framed photographs of the deceased. One wonders if this practice might also be part of the Greek Revival in this country in the early part of the last century. It was a custom in ancient Greece (5th century B.C.) to place a lock of one's hair, tied with a ribbon, on the bier of a beloved friend. Recall the classical names given American cities that came to importance some 150 years ago: Athens, in 12 states—four of them east of the Mississippi; Carthage, in 11; Corinth, Euclid, Ithaca, Omega, Orion, Seneca, Sparta, Syracuse, Troy, Utica, Xenia . . . as well as the broken columns, the sarcophagus-like tombstones, the Greek vases and drooping classical figures in marble of 19th century cemeteries.

The trappings of the doctor's horse are on exhibit—the saddle, the buggy harness, even the fly net for summer days; also his broad-brimmed heavy felt hat and the cape, ample enough to protect the horse's croup in bad weather. An Indian-cured buffalo robe from Wisconsin replaces the one which many years of service had worn to shreds. Several guns are at hand, a large medical satchel and more than one folding medicine case, fitted with small, precisely marked vials. From the dispensary, a spirit lamp remains and tiny crucibles, mortar and pestle for grinding powders, a small marble slab for the mixing and rolling of pills, and several "invalid cups" for the feeding of bed-ridden patients. A piano stool stood before his desk, on which to swing from patient to table and back.

He seems to have been highly skillful in surgery—so hazardous in those days. One can glimpse the tension between the lines of various personal items from the newspaper. "During the operation which was performed by Dr. Hutchings, the patient exhibited the utmost sang froid and left the office as if released of a burden." "Drs. Hutchings and Ennis performed the amputation [of three crushed fingers] which the patient bore manfully without taking chloroform. . . ."

The doctor fashioned his own splints for broken bones—inventing one that would strengthen a fractured clavicle; these fit neatly into a mahogany box, also made by him. Another polished box contains his Braunscheider "Lebenswecker"—the "life-restoring" electric machine previously mentioned. After his death many

Dr. Hutchings "impersonated"—Madison Centennial parade, 1911.

of his surgical instruments went to his son Robert, a physician practicing in Denver and San Francisco, and so are missing.

There are medical reports, various brochures on new medicines and methods, clippings from letters he wrote to newspapers discussing new treatments and discoveries. He insisted that tuberculosis was preventable and curable, but attacked Dr. Koch's treatment with "tuberculin" as dangerous for what we now call its side effects. Although he claimed a definite cure for diphtheria by medicine, he recommended diphtheria inoculation when used with caution.

Upon request, he published a newspaper warning to the general public in case "the cholera scourge now raging in the Old World invades Madison" (1873). He advised abstemiousness in eating and drinking but no radical change in lifelong habits; above all, a thorough cleaning and disinfection of cellars, stables and outhouses. "Talk not of quarantine, as well attempt to quarantine a cyclone. . . If the worst comes, we must throw aside cowardice, man ourselves for battle and victory. For it is written in heathen Mythology that Jove sent Pestilence to the earth to destroy 5000 [of its inhabitants]. Jove soon learned that 10,000 had been slain and called Pestilence to account for disobedience, but Pestilence affirmed his innocence and claimed that Panic came along and destroyed the other 5000." Dr. Hutchings kept his own records of vital statistics, ending his list of live births with the 2000th (two thousandth!). Official records were not instituted in Indiana until 1882. The maladies most frequently mentioned are Asiatic cholera, chills and fever, flux, pneumonia, the dread diphtheria, scarlet fever, smallpox, typhoid and typhoid-pneumonia, whooping cough and complications.

His eldest daughter Maude was his nurse and laboratory assistant for decades. At one time, the doctor asked her if she would like to "read medicine" with him. On her reply, only if she could go into practice, he said: "It is too hard a life even for a man." She was so cognizant of his methods, however, that she could pursue certain treatments on his written orders, even when he was away. After his death, she was frequently called on for various family remedies, and her prescriptions were accepted at the local pharmacy.

Sept. 7, 1899 — near Tazewell, Tenn.

My dear Daughter Maude:

Yours came on the eve of our taking the cars. We have suffered with heat, which so far is really more unbearable and greater than at home. — The F... of Dandelion is in a gallon bottle south side of shelf and must be well shaken before being poured out. For Miss G., take corrosive sublimate 7 grains even weight — not down — Iodide Potas. 2 drachms and water near 2 tablespoonsful — in a half pint bottle, add above and shake until dissolved. Then add 2½ drachms Resorcin and fill half full with the Ext. Dandelions and fill up with syrup. Dose same as before ... Love to all,

Your father

P.S. Price $2.00

A bill for drugs from the W. H. Rogers & Co. Pharmacy, from 1881 to 1883, for $101.77 in all, includes:

1 th cream of Tartar	*45¢*	*4 oz fine cut (tobacco)*	*25¢*
1 pz Cinchonidia	*75*	*4 " P. Rhubarba*	*31*
1 pz dextro quin		*violin strings*	*50*
½ th Bromide Potass	*.25*	*4 oz. Fowlers salut*	*10*
6 oz. spts & vial	*.20*	*3 grs. morphine*	*5*
2 oz. Salicin	*70*	*4 oz. iod. Potass*	*80*
¼ th tartaric acid	*.16*	*2 " sul Manganese*	*20*
Carbolic acid	*.25*	*8 pz. spts Nitre*	*25*
3 oz. brandy & vial	*.13*	*20 Vaccine points*	*2.00*

The doctor's shingle from Lexington is still at hand, listing office hours that began at 5 a.m. In Madison, his hours were from 7 to 8 a.m., 12–2, and at 7 p.m. His charges were low — "for a visit to Mrs. D. and daughter, $1.50." Even then, he did not collect from the poorer members of his practice. At his death, his daughters reckoned up that unpaid bills on his books amounted to over $50,000—a fortune for the widow with four unmarried daughters. But alas, several of Madison's most well-to-do families refused to pay when appealed to—an experience that is surely not unknown to the practitioner today.

As often, payment was made in kind. A fine leather-bound edition of Prescott's "History of the Reign of Ferdinand and Isabella the Catholic" (Boston, 1856) in three volumes is inscribed "W. D. Hutchings in payment for a surgical operation on Noah Davis." The doctor received at least four Snyder landscapes for services rendered that excellent local painter, the largest of which hung over the mantlepiece in his waiting room. William McKendree Snyder's (1848–1930) oil paintings were highly prized even in those days; Matilda's brother, Herman, wrote an offer in 1890 to exchange a Confederate sabre for one of the artist's pieces. Some years later, after the doctor's death, his daughter Lida took the paintings for signature to the old artist, who was then living in Carrollton, Ky., and on returning to pick them up, was surprised to find them signed in bright yellow.

There are a number of letters of appeal from Lexington and later:

April the 24   1875 [to Lexington]
Doctor Hutchsons   I have been sick for four months   I was taken with hot sensation and cold ones all through my systom. I have been doctering with a docter ever sinse but he has not done me much good. he has only give me medison for my head and pills to keep my bowls free. now I have hot flushing in my face and cold shivers threw my back and general weakness   my stomach weak and my tongue coated white and ringing in my ears. I want you to send me some medison and tell me if you think you can help me   write me a note. My heart is in a bad fix

Samuel Towrs
I have bad distressed feelings

Madison Ind Jan 10th 1890
Dr. Huching
   *Your Bill was duly received I am sorry I cannot settle it at once
But will try to soon, I would of settled it sooner and saved you trouble
but owing to continued sickness and dispointment of money due me it
has been imposible   Yours very respectfully*

                                             Mrs. Lottie C.

One letter especially makes one wish to know the sequence:

March the 17. 1869   [TO LEXINGTON]
*Dr. William D. Hutchings   Dear sir   i seat my self to drop you
a few lines to ask a position to read Medicine With you if it is Consis-
tant with your   i have been reading With Dr. Couperrider and as he
has left this part i would like very much to have an insight with you if
you will take me i Will try to comply With any instructions that you
should deem necessary   as Dr. Couperrider has gone to Taylorsville
it Would Bee expensive to follow him i wish to Bee Where i can stay at
home part of the time as i wish to attend to my farm in seeing that it is
cared For in a proper maner, I hav an assortment of Books But not a
suficient amount of them Wilsons anatomy, Druits surgery too volumes of Woods Practise i hav no Dictionary and i find there is not much
speed With out one. pleas let me hear from you What you think about
it in reply to this if you think Proper in due season.*

                                         Samuel H. Wilson

*the men that carried the muskets of Graham is at your back as they
Was With the Commander at the Front   Wee shall remember you
on next Tuesday and make your Majority as much as fifty   i think
Jefferson County Will give you a majority of one hundred and up-
wards do the same thing over if necessary . . . So no more at Present
but remain yours*

                                         Samuel H. Wilson
                                         Graham, Jefferson County,
                                         Ind

No follow-up was found amid the doctor's correspondence. But the fact that the letter is one of the few he kept from those early days lets one hope for a satisfactory conclusion to the young man's ambition. Such perseverence is an example of the pioneer spirit that characterized the region and the period—the Midwestern humus from which a Lincoln could emerge.

An avid interest in all scientific progress is manifest in Dr. Hutchings's numerous scrapbooks covering such various subjects as historical events, exploration, biographies of contemporary great men—often generals and presidents—as well as notes of medical achievements. In a letter to the Madison Star, he lists the "firsts" of American doctors: first to ligate the inominate artery, first to remove ovarian tumors; and he praises American dentistry as unsurpassed anywhere.

In one of those delightful social notes with which the small city newspaper of that time abounds, one reads: "On Saturday afternoon we visited Dr. Hutchings on Vine Street and had the pleasure of examining his cabinet of rare geological specimens and other curiosities. He has . . . a great many fossils of creeping things indicating the forms of animal life at various periods of the earth's formation. . . Among the curiosities which attracted our attention particularly were two scales from a saurian monster which must have been 60 feet long; the claws of a trilobite as large as a kid's hoof; ferns in rock, garnet on quartz, konchspawn and other trophies from the depths of the sea. The doctor is always pleased to meet persons interested in geology, especially if they have any specimens to exhibit or discuss." The collection of fossils, mainly from Indiana, is now in the Indiana State Museum at Indianapolis.

Dr. Hutchings is described as not tall but lithe and slim, with startlingly blue eyes. Early letters speak of his "merry lightheartedness" and of his gay laughter; of "being understood [by him] whether one talks sense or nonsense." In the memory of an old friend, "he was very handsome—wore a cape." And in a more serious vein: "His uniformly upright and honorable bearing won the confidence and respect of the community." The few letters that remain in his own hand are from later years and contain chiefly medical advice, often mentioning the weight of worry and ill health. To daughters Maude and Josephine at school in Cincinnati, just before the move to Third Street:

Madison. March 14, 1882.

My dear Children

I recd yours today. I have no news for you. The family is well as usual. Am almost worn down by the labors, cares & anxieties of my professional life and sometimes would almost welcome the repose of the grave.

Find inclosed the $50.00

Yours affectionate
Papa

To his eldest daughter, Maude:

Dec. 23, 93.   If I had been a dissembler, a cheat or less kind in my dealing with my fellow men, I would now be quite wealthy, looked up to, pandered to by the ungrateful wretches whom I have benefited. My boys know nothing of the Valley of the Shadow of Death thro which their father has passed in his childhood and pray God they may never feel it. Hence my anxiety for my children's future in this life. If my children are true to themselves . . .   then they are true to all mankind. Now my Daughter let us look to the bright side of the picture of our lives . . .

A note from the doctor to his wife dated March 16, 1897, affords a rare glimpse of the inner man. (A year earlier, their third daughter, Agnes, had married John C. Zulauf of Jeffersonville, vice-president of the Citizens Bank there.) The envelope is addressed in care of the Zulaufs in Jeffersonville, where Tillie was attending the birth of their first granddaughter, my sister Agnes. After a factual page of advice on the care of the young mother and the 2-week old child, signed "your devoted Hubby," he adds a pen-

Dr. and Mrs. Hutchings, 1890's.

cilled postscript: "With love to Agnes and John. Tell them they can now begin to feel what their parents had to go through at a certain time.

> "'In crowded halls, in festive bowers,
> In musings lone and tearful hours,
> In every change that tosses me
> With changeless love I think of thee.'"

Tillie writes from a medical convention in Washington, D.C.:

Washington City.   April 6, 1887

Dear Girls . . .   Papa took the news of John's sickness very philosophically, in fact he has abandoned all home care and is enjoying his vacation like another school boy with Dr. Woollen. You would laugh to hear them together, such laughing and funny storytelling would surprise you. We both feel in excellent health, albeit a stiffness and soreness—you would understand if you knew the amount of walking I have done...

The M.D.'s go off after breakfast to their meetings. Then Mary

[Mrs. Woollen] and myself put a lunch in our handbag "grip-sacks" and sally forth. Don't be uneasy. I array myself with care and my bonnet and attire are quite as good as the ladies I see on the street.—We ate our lunch on the gallery outside the Capitol Dome yesterday, just to eat higher than anyone else. The magnificence pictured and described give you no idea scarcely of it. We are going up Washington Monument today. . . We are going to a reception by the President—that is the M.D.'s and I think their wives. We are also to have a government boat and be taken to Mount Vernon, Washington's tomb. The Doctors are being highly honored and there are many foreign Doctors here. . . I am so delighted to see your Papa so young. He is so handsome among the other gentlemen, and I am so sorry he is not prepared to read an original article. If any Mag' comes look if any piece of his is in it. But don't read the articles in the Magazines, they will give you impressions that will always haunt you. . .

A letter to Dr. Hutchings's oldest son, Fred, from a companion gives an interesting insight into the doctor's character:

January 8, 1888
You wrote of your father being shut off from society by his duties and his books. Did it ever occur to you that your father enjoys his profession and books more than he would any society. You know he has theories of his own in regard to almost every question of the day and he don't like for anyone to have a contradictory view. I never tried to advance a theory opposite to his own but once and never expect to again. He is a man of strong likes and dislikes and to oppose him is to incur his displeasure. The very place for him is where he is and he would be miserable in other company. I admire the Doctor more than anyone I know of and would do anything for him but our tastes are a good deal alike and one does not like to mix in society more than the other. If it were not for such men as Dr. H. . . what would we do! Long live Dr. H. but I think he is as contented as he possibly could be. . .

In the late 1880's, the doctor was more than usually plagued with ill health. On October 8, 1887, he bought a cemetery lot for

Record of purchase of family cemetery lot.

himself and family, and the following spring wrote out a will, a torn fragment of which has come to light. In 1892, he suffered from the epidemic of influenza which swept that region. Several of his wife's poems reflect her concern and the attempt to reconcile herself to the inevitable parting.

Fragment of a will dated May 25, 1888:

... wife Matilda C. Hutchings,

I desire my dearly beloved children to share and share alike—equally in my estate personal and real.

I desire all my debts paid, which can readily be done without administration.

Suffering at this time with difficulty of breathing and palpitation of the heart I give the above meager indications of my last wishes with

the fear of deathe before. May the Great Father of all ever bless and guard from all evil my dearly beloved ones is the prayer of
W. D. Hutchings
When I no longer live to care for and protect, may an All Merciful God watch over and take under the shadow of His wing my dearly beloved ones whom I love more than my life. Amen.

At Dr. Hutchings's death in 1903, the Madison Star wrote a highly appreciative editorial. But his daughter Maude gives a more comprehensive picture in correspondence with a colleague of her father's in Pittsburgh.

In the early 60's he treated diphtheria with calomel and seldom lost a case... The late Dr. Mussey of Cincinnati held that since taking up our father's method, he feared diphtheria no more than an ordinary sore throat. Prior to 1870 Dr. Hutchings originated a formula of drugs for the treatment of tuberculosis, having expressed the belief that this ailment was preventable and curable—a treatment so effective that it was used up to the time of his death. In 1882 he added to the treatment, hypodermic injections of carbolic acid and atropin, and was able to save cases otherwise not to be reached by internal medicine alone. He discovered a disinfectant solution for wounds that was so efficacious that healing 'by first intention' was the usual result. In 1878, he discovered Laborandi to be a specific for yellow fever and made a spectacular cure of a riverboat captain who had arrived from New Orleans with the disease. In '79 the doctor made the first recorded cure of exophthalmic goitre, and during the influenza epidemic [1890 or 92], lost not a single patient though many were more than 70 years old and some over 80. A member of the Board of Health told the family that he had experienced several epidemics of scarlet fever and pneumonia during his service, and that Dr. Hutchings had had as many patients as the other physicians in the regions and seldom a death to report.
Our father was a remarkable surgeon. He was the first doctor to remove a dead bone and leave the periostium to make another. A two-year old child from Scott County was the patient. A portion of the

bone in his upper arm had died. The bone was cut just above the elbow and below the shoulder. The family moved away a short time after the operation and Dr. Hutchings had no report of the result. But years later an old woman who used to live at the tollgate on the other side of Hanover saw the doctor pass, stopped him and recalled herself to his mind, mighty proud of having been his nurse on that occasion. She said the muscles had grown and attached themselves to the shoulder, a new bone was secreted and the patient recovered the full use of his arm. The child's name was Hayes—and he was one of the lawyers in the notorious Pearl Bryan murder trial. . .

Maude ends her letter: "My father seldom spoke of his achievements and seldom wrote an article—he was too busy. These quiet hardworking doctors with large country clientele are many of them entirely unknown to fame forever."

Thanks to his daughters' habit of preserving what their revered father left, the Museum at Madison stands as a memorial, not only to William Davies Hutchings, but to the many valiant and ingenious — if nameless — horse-and-buggy doctors of that epic period.

PRESCRIPTIONS FOR FAMILY USE

Very few of the doctor's prescriptions remain and those are in his daughter Maude's handwriting. Perhaps she laid them aside too carefully and they disappeared from the general mass of his possessions. Perhaps they were given to his son, Robert, who had a great interest in medical history and who, after practicing in Denver, took a course in Vienna and became a successful otolaryngologist in San Francisco.

Reproduced on the following pages are some remedies jotted down by Maude, apparently for family use, together with a translation of an ancient prescription in German in the flowing hand of Matilda's doctor grandfather, Herman Koehler.

FOR CHILLS AND FEVER:

Quinna Sulph oz 1/j 1 dram
Iodide Potassium oz . . . 40 grs

$$\frac{}{1}$$

syrup ¼ pt — Whiskey ¼

Dose tablespoon before meals. Take several purgatives before commencing this.

FOR FLUX, MAY BE TAKEN EVERY FOUR HOURS:

a capsule of small dose of muriate of quinine and tiny pill blue mass. At same time take every 3–4 hours resorcin—1 rounded teaspoon in ½ glass of water, with a little glycerine added if wished.

FOR COLD:

4 drams bromide strontium, 4 oz. water — teaspoon
    3 times daily.

SORE THROAT THREATENING DIPHTHERIA:

½ cold pure water
½ peroxide of hydrogen (medicinal)
1 teasp. 4 times daily — gargle and swallow.

RECIPE FOR WHOOPING COUGH:

Linseed oil 2 oz
Orleans molasses 2 oz
Bromide potassium 1 dram or 1½ dram
Rum or whiskey 2 oz

FOR ASTHMA:

Strontium Iodide   zii
Glycerine   zi
Aqua Dist. Qt. Ad ziv
    M sig. Zi in water one to two hours P.C.

GRANDFATHER HERMAN KOEHLER'S RECIPE FOR COUGH DROPS (1818):

Take 2 oz. Spikenard
Bloodroot—1 oz—anise seed
Cabage[?]   2 oz—Liquore
       1 oz—Sulphur
       2 oz. Gumarabic
       1 oz. Ale compane[?]
       1 lb. sugar

Boil ingredients together and drain them; boil down to a syrup and then add a quart of rum to preserve it.

Hutchings sitting room, 1893.

PROSE AND POETRY

It is not easy to imagine today how limited life was in that region in the second half of the last century—what cultural resources had to be brought into play to produce entertainment, what spiritual energy and intellectual courage to face the often harsh realities, the many unknowns and bleak uncertainties. The sciences were just unfolding, the telephone was a rarity. Moving pictures, radio and television were unknown, along with other of the mass media which today reach the most out-of-the-way hamlets. The following text and pictures are offered here not so much to recite the story of a single family as to give an overview of what the situation was for many Midwestern families, whether of greater or less means.

Much of the information in these chapters derives from letters that my grandmother, Matilda C. Hutchings, wrote to her mother, and later, to her daughters. The earliest letters were tightly packed into a sturdy wooden hinged box that had once held soap. It was marked with Great-grandmother Koehler's initials and closed with a bent wire as clasp. The stamps alone earned several hundred dollars toward the restoration of the office and dispensary.

Due to the perspicacity of my Aunt Lida, the youngest surviving Hutchings, letters to and from the close family circle had been packed in separate cartons and labeled, in some cases even sorted. Here some glimpses of family life in that period are given in the protagonists' own words.

Matilda to her mother, who was then living in Madison:

> *Lexington. Christmas night, 1868.*
> *The children are fast asleep after a day of happiness. They wished me to tell you that they got Dolls that shut their eyes and Willie says "tell Ahma I have a little gun that can shoot all the rats."*
> *I put their little knives and forks under their plates and when they came to eat breakfast such joyful faces! the first thing Maude said was "write to Ahma the children have silver knives and forks." Hubby and myself spent last afternoon decorating the tree. Hubby got a little tree in the woods and brought it home, he takes as much interest in all the arrangements as myself. . .*

In 1868, Matilda's two younger sisters were teaching primary school. Aurora (1846–1928) was in her second year of work at Madison, with 40 pupils, pleased to be earning $1.75 a day—"2¢ more than last time, a pleasanter job but with more board to pay— $3. a week." Septima Vespasia (1848–1918), who at 20 held her first position in North Madison, with 50 children, "whipped only 5 boys today. . . ." In the 1890's, with the "pacification" of the prairie territories, both sisters became involved in missionary work among the Sioux. Aurora was librarian at St. Elizabeth's Episcopal School, Aberdeen, South Dakota, for many years. Septima taught at St. Mary's School, Rosebud, S.D., from 1895–98, and in the early 1900's joined her sister in Aberdeen. Their last years were spent largely in Madison with the Hutchings aunts and they both died there.

Matilda to her father, Herman Adolar Koehler, on his 66th birthday:

38

Lexington   August 1st, 1871

Dear Father

You see I have not forgotten your Birthday. I send you a birthday kiss with many wishes for your future happiness. I hope there are many happy birthdays still in store for you.

I wish when Mother comes home you would both make us a visit. I want to show you my new baby your grandson. [Herman, about 6 weeks old] He is a fine specimen of the genus-homo. Since I have a family of my own I can see what a care children are to their parents, the responsibility is fearful.

I often look over my past life and think of the trouble I have occasioned my parents and have made no return for their unwearied guardience of me. I know that I am grateful, and if my own children feel the same sentiments towards me when my head is crowned with years that I bear towards my parents I shall be satisfied.

I should like to visit you in the Fall, but my family has become so numerous that I could not unless I can leave some of them at home. If I had not such a good husband I would be crushed with care, so many depending on me; but I am grateful to be able to say that I am happier every year. . . .

Dr. is not here or he would wish to be remembered to you.

May the Almighty grant your children the pleasure of greeting you on many happy birthdays still to come is the sincere prayer of your

Affectionate daughter
Matilda.

Concern for the two children who were visiting their grandmother in Madison led to an urgent appeal, with a hint of the Doctor's proven treatment of diphtheria. This was before the discovery that inoculation alleviated the high mortality rate of this dread disease. (Two of my father's brothers died of it in Jeffersonville in the early 70's, at the ages of 9 and 11.)

Matilda to her mother in Madison:

Lexington   October 11, 1871

Dear Mother,   Your letter last night made me dreadfully nervous, so much so that I could hardly sleep. I would not be uneasy at all but for the fact that all the little children round our country have the Diphtheria in a very fatal form and the fear that Joie and Willie would get that dreadful sickness has been troubling my mind for several days. I hope Joie is now about well again and the first opportunity, as soon as she is able to go, bring them here at once, for the weather is getting unsettled and may set in rainy and the days are so short. You did not say anything was the matter with her throat or I should have been frantic. Hubby says bring them as soon as you can. He is in a perfect excitement. I am thankful that you had as skillful a Dr. as Dr. W[oollen] in whom both of us have more confidence than in any other Physician we know.

I sent a suit for Willie and a cloak and petticoat for Joie. You will find them at Swarmstedt's drugstore in a brown paper bag directed to you. The flannel [petticoat] I made last night after supper. Willie's suit is too small but he can wear another over it or under it as looks best. Get a nice pair of shoes for each and put them on, also warm stockings.

Mother, do come with them I want to see you so much. Write me right away unless you can come before next mail day. I cannot tell you how uneasy I feel although I know that you are a better nurse than myself but I have never had them so long away before.

Your affectionate daughter
Matilda.

Dr. gives more Quinine and Calomel in diphtheria than anything else and it is the best remedy he has tried. Most all his cases get well. He gives repeated doses of Calomel and Quinine, as many as 6 the first day. That is all that saves them sometimes his giving them several the second day. The throat wash — swab the throat with 40 drops of Creosote to 1 oz. of water is the throat wash.

This treatment, I might note, is affirmed in an article in the Charleston Medical Journal, Vol. 2 (1873–74) p. 33, by George E. Trescott: ". . . For myself I would state that I call no case diphtheria to outsiders, unless membrane forms. 2d, Can we, by early and powerful medication, control the disease? The general opinion was that we could not. I would say, however that Dr. Marshal,

one of the oldest and most prominent of our physicians, believes
that by calomel and quinine in large doses during the first 48 hours,
the disease can be greatly modified. . . ."

There was every reason for apprehension. Child mortality
was very high. Willie, aged ten, died of inflammatory rheumatism
in 1875, the year that little Aurora Octavia was born. Two years
later, as a letter from the hand of Maude (15 years old) tells, "the
baby" died, apparently of whooping cough which struck the entire family.

Feb. 14 Wed. 1877
Madison Jeff Co. Ind.

Dear Celia:

*Mama received your letter day before yesterday. We were sorry
to hear that you could not come right away, and hope that it will not
be long before we will see you.*

*Last 8 of Feb. our dear little baby died. The little thing died very
easy, closed its little eyes, and mouth, itself, and clasped its little hands.*

It was buried at 2 o'clock in the afternoon on the 10th.

The last word the baby said was "Mama."

*The rest of us are all better. Rob is able to sit up awhile now in
bed. Agnes and Herman still cough very badly.*

*Fred's cough is not so bad as the rest of us, he says that we took
it from him, and by the time it was divided all around, there was none
left for him.*

*Joie and I still cough very badly, and can not go to school. We
have not been to school for 5 weeks.*

*The whooping cough seems to be very bad all around, we hear of
a good many children dying of it.*

*Fred is going to school, he did not have to stop, besides the teach-
ers would not let him stop.*

*We all wish very much to see you very soon. Hoping to hear from
you soon*

I remain yours truly
Maude

*The Christmas tree was
always in the back parlor.*

In the early '80's, Joie and Agnes had typhoid fever—resulting in shaved heads and, a little later, in attractive short crops of curls.

Christmas and birthdays were made much of, though at first the gifts were modest—second-hand books and colors at 10 and 25 cents, a tin horn for Willie, which he promptly traded to Joie for her little red wagon. Later, Maude reports that her mother appeared on the scene with Bibles, prayerbooks and hymnals, fairy tales and folk stories, while father preferred bits of fur or jewelry, histories and essays—and there were always pictures from both.

Each older child assumed responsibility for one of the younger. On one occasion in the mid-70's, returning from making the doctor's rounds—for he often asked his wife to accompany him on fine days—the parents found all their children sitting on the roof-pole of the tall three-story building. My mother Agnes, a baby in arms, was among them, in the charge of Joie. When questioned, they explained that they wanted the baby to see the view. Grandmother said quietly, "Bring her down now. It is time for her supper," and went into the house so as not to excite the children with her own alarm.

Most families kept a cow, even in town. Tillie mentions two gallons at a milking and a pound of butter a day. Her chickens had the unfortunate habit of "disappearing" overnight—sometimes by two's and three's, sometimes the entire flock. She never reports them stolen. Summer was a whirl of putting up vegetables from the garden, and in the fall, the family went berrying for blackberries, elderberries, wild grapes for jelly. Peaches and pears from the back garden were made into preserves. By winter, the thick board shelves in the cellar were filled to capacity.

Considerable produce came from "the Farm" of around 150 acres near Lexington, which was conveyed to Matilda C. Hutchings in 1864 for the sum of $5000. There was a log cabin on the place and a fine stand of black walnut, said to be part of the virgin

Matilda in later years at the family farm.

forest. Especially in later years, the family enjoyed camping out in pioneer circumstances. Maude was expert in cooking at the huge open fireplace; her soda biscuits, baked in the embers in two iron skillets, one reversed over the other, remain in my memory. Although it was long rented out to tenants and the yield diminished, the Farm was the last place to be put on the market, even after the big house.

A "girl," usually from some nearby farm and inexperienced in the ways of a town, was hired to help with the heavy cleaning, cooking and scrubbing which the housewife supervised. All clothing was fashioned at home, at least at first. Tillie writes of finishing numberless nightgowns and petticoats, of a little suit made from one of Papa's old ones for Willie, and gowns dressed up with a new Bertha or a lace collar, a hat with a red and white feather for $2.50. For the doctor's birthday in 1870, she embroidered him a beaded watch case on scarlet velvet in the shape of a slipper.

Three of the several quilts from the big house have interesting histories. A free design of scattered tulips and a colorful interpretation of the Rising Sun in various shades of red are the work of "Auntie Boothe," a mulatto freedwoman. Daughter of a plantation owner's son and a slave girl in the deep South, she was sent North by her grandfather and lived a long and fruitful life as a practical nurse in the community. She was particularly devoted to Mrs. Hutchings and wrote to Maude in 1893: "Your mama knows how much love I send to her, for there is no lady in the town for whom I have more."

Another quilt is mentioned by Maude in 1900 as "the John Quincy Adams quilt, gift of Miss Martha, with papers concerning it—so big that it covers the entire bed." Though "the papers" do not survive, the Rose of Sharon pattern fits the description, at least in size and Federal tradition.

A room was set aside in the Third Street house for the children and their games. Halloween was a time of special gaiety and elaborate costumes, designed and executed by the two older sisters. A wonderful doll's house delighted young and old, with the pony-size rocking horse which was given away years ago.

44

"Auntie Boothe," a freedwoman.
DAGUERREOTYPE.

"Pomegranate," a traditional 19th Century quilt design.

Agnes, 14, with violin, 1888.
DAGUERREOTYPE.

Christmas carols with Joie at the harmonium, ca. 1900.

An old friend who was much at the house tells that Matilda would go to the office at dinner time and "escort the Doctor in, so stately as to a wedding feast." Maude would be already in the dining-room to greet and seat the guests who followed host and hostess.

A zither, two violins, a guitar and a banjo were found in the house. Maude, Fred, Agnes and Lida played the violin; Tillie, the guitar. In April, 1880, Fred notes buying a violin, bow and case for $5.50. Several members of the family played the piano adequately by ear. Joie had a smooth alto voice; Zoe, a heavier dramatic one; Agnes, a remarkable high soprano. She sang in church and generally took the lead in the operettas that were given in the enterprising town. Some training in Cincinnati was aspired to but never came to pass.

Herman and Lida were both excellent photographers. The collection of their cameras, tripods, developing tanks and printing frames, on exhibition at the Museum, is notable. Lida sold a number of her scenes for post cards. Many of the illustrations in the chapter, "Golden Dust," were taken by the two.

Discipline was unobtrusive but firm. When Agnes, age about 19, was entertaining a swain in the front parlor, someone passed

Herman, taking picture of self and friends, with tube and squeeze bulb, 1892.

through the back parlor and struck a single note on the old square piano there. "That is G," said Agnes, rising, "it means GO. . . ." Later, visiting a friend in Jeffersonville, she was courted by the next door neighbor. In describing the visit upon her return she mentioned going out driving with him. Someone remarked, "Agnes, you know your mother would never allow you to drive out alone with a man unless you were engaged," and so the secret engagement—to John Zulauf, my father—came out sooner than intended.

At the age of 18, Fred left home for the East to carve out for himself a career as electrical engineer. Both father and mother were in considerable trepidation at sending their eldest son out into the wicked world. But upon Fred's report of his first steady, paying job, the doctor responded with enthusiasm in one of the few letters that survive in his own handwriting.

Madison, Ind. Feb. 14—1887

All hail my brave boy. You have done nobly. A forward and honorable course have won you a fine reputation in your native place and will continue to keep you in high places in the estimation of good men.

I have constantly thought of and watched your course with great solicitude and anxiety, fearing the dangers, and temptations surrounding your inexperience but now—thank the Giver of all Good—I feel easy—and proud of my brave son

Your father

Details of Fred's work appear in a letter written shortly after his 19th birthday:

North Adams, Mass.   June 14, 1887

My dear Father:

. . . I am paid by the hour, so the longer I work the better I am rewarded. On Sundays we get double time, two hours for one, that of course is a great inducement. I received a raise in wages two weeks ago. It was very unexpected. I am now paid $3.25 Per day—.32½ cts Per hour. There is not one wireman in a dozen who gets that much & very

48

few who get more, but I don't take it as much of a compliment to my-self, because wiremen as a rule are a very ignorant set of men, of little schooling or culture...

Subsequent letters show the young man's progress through the East, including New York City, Buffalo, and Wilmington. He and his younger brother, Herman, bought and worked an orange grove at Hernando, near Ocala, Florida (1893). Young Lida, who was judged in need of a change of climate, went with them. That was frontier living with a vengeance—and they all enjoyed it. She describes riding to town in a buckboard with a rifle across her knees with which to shoot rabbits for dinner. However, there was not capital enough to carry the venture safely through several years of poor harvest.

Following the trend of the times, Fred is then heard of in the West. At that time, his sister Josephine, confidante and comforter of the entire family, was studying at the University of Chicago for a teaching certificate. With her, he is less circumspect than with his parents. From Dallas he reports that his crew have put in a plant at Eagle Pass—"mechanical side easy, but business part brings gray hairs—$11,000 to collect & we expect trouble. . ."

The doctor congratulates his son Fred, 1887.

Dear Joie

Your very sweet letter of late date came to hand and did me more good than any letter I have received in an exceedingly long time. Why this prelude, my dear girl? because you expressed approval of me, that is you were satified that I had done nothing wrong & had no in-born inclination to do so.

Do you know that letters from home especially parental letters always give me the feeling that I am on a sort of term of probation, my nature being so perverse as to render constant "coaching" necessary to keep me in the path of recticude.

In the event of my having trouble with my bosses and I write the affair to dad in detail, his reply will show me up in the wrong every time. . . . If I fall into a blissful state of transient love, which occurs about every time a petticoat appears on the horizon, and write to mama about it, the reply is a long lecture on women, their habits and uses, what of their manifold traits to admire and what to look upon with suspicion. She gives me terrible warnings and no credit for any taste or higher instinct which would protect me.

So it is a great encouragement to be patted on the back occasionally whether you are right or wrong. —A person always knows when they are in the wrong & they feel grateful in being upheld in it. The feeling of gratitude is a noble trait and will prompt a confession of wrong, while to be reminded of the wrong prompts stuborness, a man gets pigheaded over it and swears he is right until he believes it himself.

A cold wave struck us about a week ago —12 below zero and 3 feet of snow. I will always be grateful though owing to many delightful sleighrides with the woman I love (married). I have never really loved before this time. She knows nothing about it, doubtless thinks of me when she sees me which is encouraging. My sentiment has lasted several months, a constancy surprising. Rob says you are looking fine and becoming quite world wise. I am of the earth, earthy and so is he.

. . . I confess I have been here almost 15 months & never been to church once. At one time I started to church after receiving one of mama's letters but on the way discovered a car off the track. My sanctity was at once changed into reviling and imprecations. It illustrated

the inconsistency of things, too—to keep the car in the straight and narrow way (that leads to the power house) I myself must travel the broad and crooked highway leading to saloons and general destruction.

At the hotel tonight, the Bachelors' Ball (ball of the season) is in progress. I did not subscribe the $7.50 to it because I have no dress suit & and no money to buy one with. I will look on from the balcony & see the $40.00 stool pigeons prance around with homely girls. The girls around this country are the most scraggly, measly looking set I ever saw & and such society, they have not even decent table manners. . . .

Here it might be told that Fred eventually became Superintendent of the Vancouver tramway and light system.

Letters from the younger brother, Rob, show a more buoyant nature. From his first position after graduation from medical school:

Cincinnati Hospital—April 11, 1892

Dear Father—

. . . Yesterday was my first day on duty at the hospital—that is the 1st day on which I had charge of the patients myself. The patients seemed to all immediately get worse—3 had temperatures rush up to 104 and over—two more had violent hysterical attacks and very likely, had I taken my own temperature, I should have found it as high as any of theirs. The pulse rate was something wonderful—I expected that an epidemic of deaths would immediately take place. Fortunately for me, they are still alive and doing finely today—of course I ascribe it to my treatment—that is the usual way I believe: if a patient dies it is Providence, if he lives, it is the Doctor. What egoists we mortals are!

The fluctuations of my spirits is something marvelous. One time I go through the wards and I think I know something—and that it would be fine to have some serious cases on hand. Next round (an hour or so later) I conclude I am an ignoramus of the worst sort and would be afraid to see an ordinary uncomplicated case of measles.

Like his brother, Rob soon sought his golden opportunity in the West:

Dear Mother —

Your letter of recent date wherein you gave an account of your experiences with fire reached me safely — glad you escaped without loss of anything. — I have seen those fires & know what they do. Was out on the plains once, with a bunch of people, horseback. chasing coyotes. One fellow lighted a cigar and dropped the match & and like a flash the whole place was ablaze — & it took some very hard hustling to stop the fire from spreading over the whole landscape. . . .

I just returned from a trip of three days — had 120 miles staging and 60 miles railroading. Picked up a man on the road suffering from appendicitis. He staged it about 50 miles & then took train for Salt Lake City his home. He is apt to die — maybe is dead now.

To his sister Joie:

11 1st 1896   #1424 N. Nevada Ave.,
Colorado Springs Colo.

. . . From all appearances I shall make a go of it here. The place is full of life and bustle & there is lots of money. I am going out next week & stake out a claim for a gold mine. There may be nothing in it & there may be thousands & as it don't cost me much to do this I shall try my luck. In a week or so I shall be in an office of my own & ready to practise medicine. My name will appear in the paper giving me a good puff & citing my wonderful experience etc. with the accent on the etc. & I shall see what gold I can coin from the populace. . . . It was "Pikes Peak or bust" in the olden days — and I am on Pikes Peak and practically busted — but as I am sure of 3 meals a day and a bed, I have no fear that in a few years I'll be owning a house & lot of my own. Joie, don't take life so seriously, it don't pay. I feel as jolly now as I did when I had $500. cash in my pocket. Worry don't pay, no matter how desperate things look. . .

Thwarted in her desire to become a physician, for which she showed real talent, Maude studied taxidermy. A fine shot with a rifle, she made a collection of the birds of Southern Indiana which

"Faust" in the Hutchings living room.

she set up in lifelike groups together with their nests and eggs. These were later given to Earlham College at Richmond, Indiana. She also modeled a group of animals in plaster and covered them with cloth, appropriately textured and painted. But these have long fallen prey to time, to moths, and the fondling of delighted children.

Maude to Joie in Chicago:

January 2
My first letter of the New Year—the much-lauded be-flattered New Year that half the time is like all spoiled infants, hoped much from and disappointing, caressed and ungrateful, constantly spoken of and not responsive, always promising and lying. . .

Last night the children entertained their club and invited Robin, Robert and Maurice besides. Then Mary W. was visiting at the Hen-

nessey's and Georgie, a cousin at the Fentons, so they came too. There were 13 at table—and Frank grabbed me by the arm and urged me to eat at the same time. So I drank chocolate-between waiting on them and thus saved the superstitious some fears. . . . All were dressed in some sort of costume or fancy rig. Zoe said she was Josiah Allen's wife and looked it. She wore her "Old Woman in a Shoe" costume from the Mother Goose Market [a public "entertainment" of the year before] and an old straw bonnet of Mama's, tied with great plaid streamers under the chin. . .

Helen had no costume so I fixed her up as a Jap with her hair in a long pig tail with heavy ribbons dangling from the point of it and one peacock feather waving. The Fentons and their visitors had to bring their things to dress and had ever so much fun in the red room getting themselves done up. As Sallie M. had no costume, I put her into Agnes's "Mary Quite Contrary" dress. Robert wore leggings, fez, and sash from some drill he had been in and Robin wore Herman's dragon costume. We could hardly get him into it and he couldn't sit down. His wings tore the mistletoe off the chandeliers and almost put out the girl's eyes in the dancing. Maurice was in his undress uniform from the Military school he is attending.

We lighted up the tree and passed around a box of mixed candies. The rugs were rolled up, furniture pushed to the wall and the girls took turns at the piano or Lida on the violin. Soon after I had them come out to the dining room and served them (on Mama's new plates) salted wafers and little cups of chocolate, olives, dates, fig cake and macaroons. We used the little cups and after-dinner spoons (some for the first time) and Mama's beautiful orange spoon for the sugar. I was delighted with our children's manners and the cute things they did and said.

Tuesday noon— . . . We have decided to let the kids have their celebration of Twelfth Night. Next Thursday is Epiphany and we will have the club in the afternoon and not put out any regular refreshments. We can get one of those plain pound cakes from Gertz or Winnefield and I will punch a bean into it from underneath. The one who gets the bean is King or Queen and chooses his partner for that day. I will have two crowns ready and the cake will be served as soon as they all arrive. They will have little seed cakes as is done in England and candy from the tree. I have a lot of colored candles that came at different times and we didn't use and shall burn those in the parlors. The day is often called Candlemas or Little Christmas. We will put fresh candles on the tree and light them up and they can tell fortunes as the Russians do on this day. Mama is going to write some rhymes for the fortunes. Then they will want to dance as usual. . .

Amid her many duties with household and her large family, Matilda found the time and energy to "scribble incessantly." While sitting with a sick child, when sewing, or waiting for the doctor at home or in the buggy on one of his calls, she jotted down verses— on the backs of old envelopes or bits of wrapping paper. Some appeared in the local newspapers and in anthologies of Indiana poets. She published also a number of short stories in Hoosier dialect, but none of these have come to hand although they are mentioned in several letters. Especially charming are her many Christmas poems, full of wonder and delight. Couched in the idiom of the time, her writing is unpretentious and sincere and shows a marked musical sense.

Matilda's "scribbling" —poem ms. in pencil on envelope.

DAGUERREOTYPE.

to W.D.H.

In the cold moonlight the dark shadows lie,
the lonely night bird for her absent mate's grieving;
sad zephyrs catch the soft echoes and sigh
toying with garlands night's fingers are weaving.

Since the first star smiled a welcome tonight,
and her pale sisters silently came, one by one,
I've watched for thy coming, I list for thy step,
for when thou art absent, I feel all alone.

Deeper the shadows fall, dark grows the night—
I seek mid the gloom thy loved form to descry.
Slowly and sadly the hours wear on—
I cannot be happy unless thou art nigh.

Tillie
February 14, 1862

*. . . I want to go with you when our children are large enough
to leave at home.*

Soft as the gentle air of summer's eve,
sweet as the fragrant breath of early flowers,
bright as the visions that fond lovers weave,
buoyant and happy as youth's glowing hours,
    are all my thoughts, my love, of Thee!

Of Thee alone my heart has learned to sing,
sweet is the song and soft the echo's wake,
lingering like some charmed radiant thing
forever loth the dearest spell to break —
    the spell that binds my soul to Thee!

Thy dearest thoughts are ever thoughts of me —
O ever blest, my love alone is mine!
And wert Thou wandering over land and sea
still would my spirit feel the glow of thine,
    such ties do bind my soul to Thee!

*The rest is unwritten music left to your own imagination.—I
have been interrupted by visitors—Mrs. E. . . and her sister
from Kansas. I must now hasten to close my letter as it is
nearly dark. The children speak of you every day and are
trying to learn so as to gratify you on your return. I send you
many kisses and hope soon to have the happiness of giving
them to you in person.*

                                    Your loving Wife
                                    M. Hutchings.

P.S. I think love letters are nice.

                                    January 31, 1873

NEWBORN

The long hot days with swooning hours
had passed, and with the summer's flowers
    had slipped away.
With goldenrod to mark her tread
with stars and asters on her head,
    and veil of gray,
September with her courtly mein, has come to stay.

But all the gifts of earth and air
can never with this one compare—
    this gift of mine:
like to the mild September skies,
this tender blue of baby's eyes,
    this look divine.

On brow so smooth, so guileless fair,
lie tiny curls of yellow hair,
    a halo such as angels wear.
Her dimpled hands, her dainty feet,
pink toes and fingertips, complete
    a miniature, surpassing sweet.
Such innocent, yet gracious mien
in loving hearts have made her queen—
so then we named her: Josephine.

WIDE AWAKE

My mother wishes me to sleep, but I
    have always hated sleep;
and since she knows 'tis so, I wonder why
    she rocks me, till to keep
my eyelids up I cannot even try.

Just when its getting dark is best to play,
    for then you want to do
so many things you can't when it is day.
    You feel so waked up too.

I love to catch the lightning bugs and run
    hard races with the moon,
then hide in grass—not let her see she's won.
    (Dew always falls too soon.)

Indeed, were there no dew, I sometimes think
    that mother would not care
how late I stay outdoors and try to wink
    so fast as stars and stare

Like them, or mock the katydids or frog
    that sounds so queer and hoarse.
Why, even Rover likes the night—our dog—
    and wants to play, of course.

But mother says that bed's the proper place
    for little boys at night.
So in I have to come and wash my face,
    when O not yet a mite
too sleepy! Mother rocks me though, in case. . .

MADISON HERALD.

Madison, Ind., Dec. 31, 1898.

For The Herald.

Good-bye, Old Year, Good-bye.

For all the good that thou hast wrought,
For precious gifts that thou hast brought,
For that full cup of brimming sweet,
For rapture, though 'twere all too fleet,
For joys that bade the angels sing,
That gave to life its zest and spring,
Deep in our hearts thou hast a place
Sacred to thee, fair with the grace
Of the best loved, forever dear.
  Goodbye, old Year. Goodbye, old Year.

For all the ill that thou hast wrought,
For all the sorrow thou hast brought,
For wreakage and for treasure lost,
For scars unhealed the battle cost,
For that pale phantom from the gloom
And chill of death, for blighted bloom,
And tears, whose drops scorched as they
    fell,
For griefs that have no words to tell,
We must, we do forgive thee here.
  Goodbye, old Year. Goodbye, old Year.
          —M. C. HUTCHINGS.

THE HERALD.

JOHN ADAMS. - - - Proprietor

L. C. JONES, Lessee. Editor and Publisher

MADISON, JANUARY 29, 1897.

JANUARY NIGHT.

[For the Madison Herald.]
Against the heart of Winter pressed
By icy arms and breath carressed
    Night lieth chilled.
There's lustrous glint within star-eyes
Where an imprisoned tear drop lies
    Frozen, unspilled.

The sky—a brow so calm, so cold—
A Death-masque seems its frigid mould;
    The floating hair
Trailing its length as dusky cloud,
Draping, clinging, as 'twere a shroud
    Had frozen there.

The river with a fickle art
Traces Night's image on its heart
    Frail as a sigh;
On heights where Æons vigils keep,
Pale ghost of an unresting sleep,
    The moon goes by.
          —M. C. HUTCHINGS.

THE SMELL OF THE CEDAR

The Christmas garlands hang on the wall,
the smell of the cedar is over all.
The dearest visions I see tonight,
the radiant visions of Holy Night!
The dearest voices I hear again.

* * *

The patter of feet on stairway and hall,
the echoing cadence of laughter and call,
the mistletoe hanging high over the way,
it was cleft from an ancient oak that day.
A bounteous table, benignly stored,
the group of children around the board—
(the burdened tree well the secret kept
how we filled its boughs while the children slept.)
I hear the bell in the tower ringing
the choir in the organloft is singing,
the voice of the priest and people in prayer.
A woodsy fragrance pervades the air.
From altar to portal, from wall to wall,
the smell of the cedar is over all.   *M.C.H.*

EASTER MORNING.

A voice speaks to thy soul:
  "Leave this closed mound.
The tide of time will roll
  Thy barque beyond
Into a quiet harbor, where the sea
Obeys the voice of Him on Galilee.
The cross forget, the crown of thorns,
  The blood drops, spear-thrust in
    the side,
The agony that mourns
  When Love is crucified,
The bitter tears of sorrow's own ap-
  pointing,
Tears, heart-wrung tears, the chrism
  for love's annointing."

This morning in the East
  A glory rose,
As through some ardent quest
  Heaven would disclose
The passion of rare beauty, satisfying
All that the soul conceives in glori-
  fying.
Morning of life, the life
  That mortals crave,
The gladdest Spring is rife
  In open grave,
The song of Life, its harmony of
  ecstasy.
The Dead shall live in love, in life's
  eternity.
            M. C. HUTCHINGS.

MADISON HERALD.

Madison, Ind., April 7, 1898

August In The Garden.

I know an old garden of flowers
  In rioting crowds, colors gay,
Sun-flushed, and with sparkle of showers,
  And sweet in the old-fashioned way.

An apple tree leans in an angle.
  Wild creepers entwined with the hop,
The white and the green in a tangle,
  Cling sportive and swing from the top.

And day after day August sunlight
  Gave fullness to ripen and prime.
And night after night August moonlight
  Wrought mysteries from fancy's own
    clime.

There was preening, coquetting, adorning
  In the garden—until one day
All unnoticed, so subtle the warning,
  Fleet August slipped out and away.

Sunflowers' brown eyes looking earthward,
  Under frills that have lost their flare,
See rust-spotted blades in the green sward
  And fallen leaves here and there.

Deeper shades on verbena and zinnia
  The "old man" is putting on grey;
Less trim are the phlox and petunia,
  But sweet in the old-fashioned way.
          —M. C. HUTCHINGS.

IN MY GARDEN

In my garden, all a-tangle,
crowd to wall's remotest angle
    violet, lily, poppy, rose.
Colors riot, bluejays wrangle
    from early Spring to Summer's close.

O what wooing in my garden,
in this blooming leafy Arden,
    stirring days of early Spring!
Lovers quarrel, lovers pardon —
    'tis the way of world a-wing.

In my garden red-bird's trilling
sets my listless heart a-thrilling
    wakes again old joys long dead —
woodbine's scented breath distilling
    breath of all the summers fled.

To my garden's pomp and splendor,
to its sounds and scents and tender
    wealth of violet, lily, rose,
all my senses homage render,
    from early Spring to Summer's close.

"KNOW'ST THOU THE LAND.."

Know you the place where rest secure is found,
where toil is eased of galling fretting strain?
where care is solaced and the aching wound
finds balm to sooth with kind surcease of pain?
Where love has voice sweetest to mortal ear,
where truth in whitest garments is adored —
where faith keeps step by day and robs the night of fear
and hope brings flowers to deck the daily board?

Know you the place? for if you do not know,
then life withholds from you its chiefest boon —
wealth of the Inds such gift cannot bestow,
that gift of heaven whose name on earth is Home.

This poem was sent to Fred in Vancouver.

SONG OF THE DOLLAR

O the dollar, the dollar, the precious gold dollar,
the dollar of the proper yellow hue,
the neat shiny dollar of standard weight and color,
the sound honest dollar, ringing true.

O the dollar, the dollar, the bright silver dollar,
the round silver dollar that we know—
the plump silver dollar like the moon in shape and color,
with a face that no other moon can show.

O the dollar, the dollar on the land and on the water,
esteemed in all its phases as a rule.
Dear to every son and daughter in the half and in the quarter,
and altogether lovely in the full.

O the dollar, the dollar, the ever welcome dollar,
the only tramp that all are glad to see
at all times and every season, within or without reason,
the undisputed open sesame.

O the dollar, the dollar, on whatever earthly stages
such a talismanic power is in the name,
despite all saws and sages of all nations in all ages—
'tis the almighty dollar just the same.

DRIFTING

Afloat, beneath the open sky
within my idle skiff I lie:
Before my gaze the panoramic spread
of river, towering hills and overhead
white fleecy cloudlets sailing by.

Like tiny speck within the blue
I see a hawk. Now downward through
the air he drops, then wheels away
on lazy wings. Yet still my gaze will stray
in search to follow where he flew.

BOUNCING BETTY

Along the Ohio River's side,
on the banks above the highest tide,

the road leads on as the river wills
and skirts the feet of the high steep hills.

Here the bonny Bouncing Bettys grow —
and art and culture they never know.

They are not trammeled with cords and stays
to form and fashion of garden ways,

nor plucked from the place they love the best,
to droop and die on a heartless breast.

All summer, safe from city strife,
they live the freedom of rustic life.

Where the Ohio River graceful sweeps
past wooded slopes and rocky steeps,

where the pawpaw bush and the sumac grows
and sweet briar guards her wee pink rose,

where swaying branches keep time to the breeze
in the shadow dance, under grand old trees, —

Nature's own loveliness is such
as makes one long for the artist's touch.

And among the charms that will please the eye,
regaling the heart of the passer-by,

are the Bouncing Bettys of scant renown
on the river roadside just out of town.

You can see them there any summer day
when it suits your pleasure to pass that way.

September, 1891

APRIL MAID

In the west the clouds have drunk their fill
From bending river that flows at will
Past the rocky peak and wooded hill.
    A soft grey mist
Floats out of the west and the light grows dim,
Grey fold on fold hides the horizon's brim,
Where the earth and sky on the fartherest rim
    Have met and kist.

The wilful zephyr swift flies and sings,
Scattering raindrops with fluttering wings,
Splashing the river with circling rings.
    A rifted shade
Slips from the east,—lo, burst of light,
Of red sunbeams, of blue and white,
A fitful vision—witching sprite,
    The April Maid.

JUNE

A wide blue sky where whitest clouds go by,
    south winds in warm waves flowing,
The song of the meadowlark clear and high,
    Red clover ripe for mowing.
Wild roses revel of softest pink,
    the scarlet trumpet's a-blowing,
on cool moist brink where the cattle drink
    the calamus sprouts are growing.

The lingering days in the sun's red rays,
    and Nature repleted, sighing,
the murmurous ways in the twilight haze
    when wild wings are homeward flying.
Fair Venus walks with the radiant moon;
    night's fingers carressing, tender,
lay a spangled cover on sleeping June
    at rest from her day of splendor.

1897

CLIFTY CREEK IN AUTUMN

There's no lovelier valley wherever you seek
Nor a stream that's more fair than our own Clifty Creek.
The valley lies deep in the heart of the hills
with varying charms of each mood Nature wills.
'Twixt hills grand with trees, and rocks jutting over,
where wild tangled vines trip the feet of the rover,
There, far from its source, fresh and buoyant as ever
runs the cool crystal stream till it reaches the river.
Now glancing, now dancing in holiday fashion,
then the deep steady current of purpose and passion.

You think with a thrill and your heart's warmest beat—
could there be any other on earth half so sweet
as the valley you know with the golden days there,
when the last sigh of summer still quivers in air—
any stream that so gladdens the heart of a lover
as our own Clifty Creek on its way to the river
with tinkle and wrinkle, with whisper and laughter,
always going and flowing and more coming after,
now with song soft entrancing with grace notes enhancing,
then the full tide and sweep of a grand march advancing.

Where sycamores lean, the spent water lingers
encircling the roots as with rings the long fingers.
When laggards grow many, overcrowded for space,
slipping over the brim they join ranks in the race
down long hazy vista, under skies tend'rest blue
where a light that from somewhere near Heaven shines through.
As the voice and the face of the loved to the lover
is our own Clifty Creek on its way to the river.

1886

"TILL DEATH DO US PART.."

I will not be lost to thee though I have died,
though life's sun is set and the dark eventide
    is the shadow of death.
Though quiet and cold as the stone at my head,
my pillow unrumpled, my deep narrow bed
    unstirred with a breath,

I will not be lost to thee though I have died.
There is that will hold me alway to thy side —
    and stronger than death —
the tie so mysterious that binds soul to soul,
as true as the needle that turns to the Pole,
    and vital as breath.

I will not be lost to thee though I have died.
Doubt not! There is in God's universe wide,
    unshadowed by death,
that communion of spirit that blesses the earth,
is perfection, where love has its home and its birth,
    and immortal breath.

September 18, 1892

Anna Christine Kuehnen   *John Henry Ludeling*

FAMILY ALBUM

No daguerreotypes and very few letters remain from the doctor's childhood. It appears that he lost all his nearer relatives at a comparatively early age.

More extensive records remain of Matilda's ancestry. Her father's family migrated from Württemberg, Germany, to Baltimore in 1819, when he was 14. Her mother's parents—John Henry Ludeling and his wife, the former Anna Christine Kuehnen, pictured above—came from Bremen to New Orleans in 1810 or 1812. Family tradition tells that Mrs. Ludeling journeyed down the Opelousa River to join her husband, who had settled in Pointe Coupée Parish, Louisiana. She was escorted by a former English officer with an Indian guide called Plume Blanche. Through the officer's faulty loading of their canoe, the vessel overturned and he was drowned. Plume Blanche rescued the young woman and took her to a nearby Indian village where she was cared for by the native women until able to proceed. For years thereafter, Plume Blanche visited the family at intervals, bringing gifts—such as a fine double-woven basket which was handed down through generations.

Matilda's mother, Aurore Gerhardine Ludeling Koehler (1814–1890), born at Pointe Coupée, La.

DAGUERREOTYPE.

Matilda's favorite brother, Herman Charles Koehler (1835–ca. 1916), in his later years.

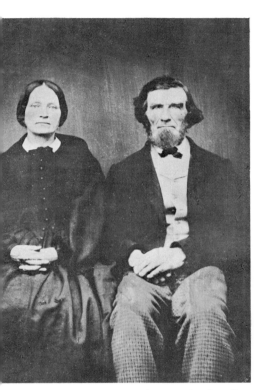

Matilda's parents, Aurore Gerhardine and Herman Adolar Koehler (1805–1882).

DAGUERREOTYPE.

The four Koehler daughters (Matilda, seated, left), ca. 1865.

DAGUERREOTYPE.

Aurora Koehler in the 1860's.
DAGUERREOTYPE.

. . . and in the 1880's.

Septima Vespasia Koehler (left) in the 1870's.

DAGUERREOTYPE.

...and in 1896.

148 W. 4th ST.   CINCINNATI, O.

Robert Henry Koehler, Matilda's younger brother . . .

148 W. 4th ST.   CINCINNATI, O.

...and his bride, Lida Gano, 1870's.

Maude (seated left) and Josephine (standing left) at Miss Nourse's School in Cincinnati in the late 1870's.
DAGUERREOTYPE.

Maude, age 25.

... and 10 years later, with first niece.

"*Little Willie*," (*1865–1875*).
DAGUERREOTYPE.

Josephine, age 24.

FRED

Fred became an electrical engineer. He helped install the trolley
system in Wilmington, Del., and
kept blueprints of its luxurious private car (upper and middle right).
After serving as president of the
tramway system in Vancouver,
Canada, he became an official of
the North American Chemical
Company and of the power company in Bay City, Mich. At lower
left, he watches his future wife
light the first fires at one of the
firm's plants (Sept. 1, 1898). At
lower right, he drives an early
electric automobile.

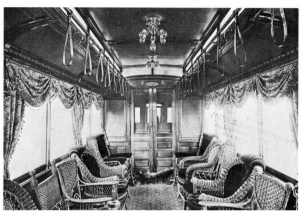

Robert was a light-hearted soul. In the picture above, he stands at the far left, derby at a jaunty angle, with the Class of 1887, Hanover College, Ind., gathered at Clifty Falls. His close friend, elegant Fred Hennessy, sits at far right in front. Lower picture shows Robert in later life.

ROBERT & HERMAN

Herman, shown in two views above, was a civil engineer and an excellent photographer—author of many of the illustrations in this book. His picture below shows a friend at a mine head in the gold fields of Cripple Creek, Colo., in the 1890's.

ENTER ZULAUFS:
AGNES MARRIES

John C. Zulauf (1818–1873), Swiss vice-consul in Glasgow, Scotland, traveled to Indiana in 1846 to settle legal affairs of Swiss colonists in Clark, Jefferson and Switzerland Counties . . . and decided to stay. He was appointed "Swiss consul to the Western States" and eventually settled in Jeffersonville, serving as president of the Jeffersonville, Madison & Indianapolis Railroad. Shown below are engagement photographs of his son, John C. Zulauf, and Agnes Matilda Hutchings, 1895.

DAGUERREOTYPE.

Agnes "pours" at an engagement party.

The first Hutchings granddaughter.

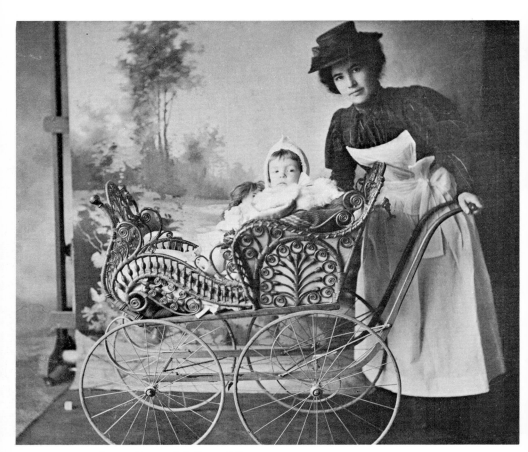

Agnes, Jr., and doll go riding.

Agnes and Elisabeth Zulauf (standing) with two household pillars— maid and cook—at summer cottage on the Knobs, ca. 1902.

Lida with Fred at Agnes's wedding.

Lida, age 9. Her doctor father let her sing German songs to his patients.

Zoe in her graduation dress.

...and later, costumed for a play.

"Excuse Us"   DAGUERREOTYPE.

Neighborhood Sketches

By WALTER H. KISER.

The Hutchings House, Madison, Ind.

Lida Hutchings, 1951.

Her last photo —
with niece Elisabeth Zulauf Kelemen, 1956.

Pioneer home, built in 1805 at Clifty Canyon, near Madison.

GOLDEN DUST

I'm told in riding somewhere West,
A stranger found a Hoosier nest—
In other words, an old log cabin
Just big enough to hold Queen Mab in.

[ANONYMOUS]

Dr. Hutchings's buggy no longer rolls over the ruts of farm roads, and the eight white horses with the circus wagon no longer parade down Main Street, gilded by the Midwestern sun. The dust they stirred up has settled on those times. In the beautifying perspective of the decades, some of it has turned to gold.

TRANSPORTATION FOR LARGE AND SMALL

Grandma Grafe.

C. C. Jones and family.

Elbert Prater and family.

Road to the ferry.

Madison from the Hanover Road.

Overhung Rock on Hanover Road.

Watering trough on Hanover Road.

Camping at the creek.

Minstrel's parade, 1892.

ADMINISTRATION BLDG., NEW INSANE HOSPITAL, MADISON, INDIANA.
FOLTZ & PARKER, ARCHITECTS, INDLPS.

THE EGGLESTON SCHOOL, MADISON, IND.
DEDICATED OCT. 3, 1907. H. M. Flora, Photo.

Main Street looking east.

Small business.

Mock-up for newspaper advertisement of a new store.

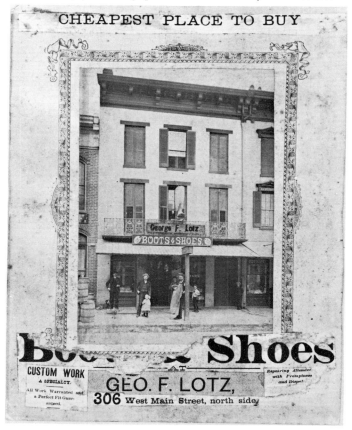

Southern Indiana farm country.

Bob Bailey and bride.

OHIO RIVER IN VARIOUS MOODS AND SEASONS

The Big Bend from Hanover.

Surrey.

Hack.

Brougham.

Buggy.

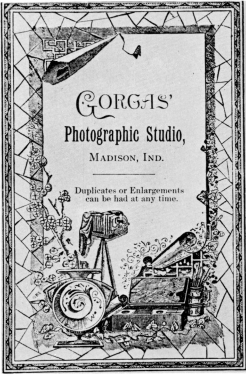

Elegance was not only in the photograph itself, but also on the back of the mounts.

Gorgas,   Madison, Ind.

Sulky race.

Rendezvous.

Card club, 1891.

Big cut on the J.M. & I. Railroad.

"German band."

DESCRIPTION OF THE NEOGRAPH

Its Construction and Operation.

IN DESIGNING THE NEOGRAPH we adopted the stylus as the foundation principle, as it is much simpler, less danger of getting out of order than a complicated wheel-pen and less costly if it has to be replaced.

The NEOGRAPH belongs to that class of duplicators using the stencil process. The stencil is made on a sheet of finely waxed paper.

A sheet of stencil paper is stretched in a stretching frame which stretches the paper evenly in all directions, perfectly taut. The frame stretching the

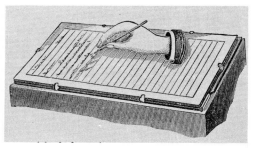

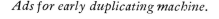

Ads for early duplicating machine.

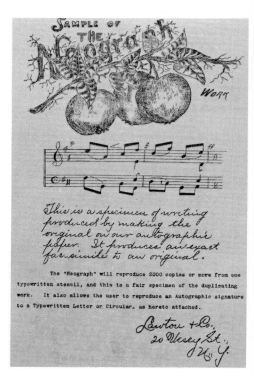

Sentimental souvenirs.

Summer idyll.

Waiting at the ferry.

"Remember Me."

NOTES ON THE ILLUSTRATIONS

PAGE 1.
The side-wheeler, *City of Louisville,* was the sister ship.

PAGE 19.
Family picture for the doctor's 60th birthday, 1885:

LEFT TO RIGHT, FRONT:	Agnes Matilda	(1874–1933)
	Herman Woollen	(1871–1902)
MIDDLE ROW:	Zoe Augusta	(1880–1961)
	Josephine Lillian	(1863–1930)
	Matilda	(1840–1914)
	Maude	(1862–1931)
	Lida	(1878–1968)
STANDING, REAR:	Robert Koehler	(1869–1956)
	Charles Frederick	(1868–1948)

PAGE 22.
The doctor's impersonator in the 1911 centennial parade was Nick Klein, who wore the doctor's paraphernalia and rode the Hutchings horse "Bess."

PAGE 53.
"Faust" in the Hutchings living room: Robin Graham as Mephistopheles, Sallie Marshall as Gretchen, Zoe Hutchings as Arent.

PAGE 66.
Picnic beyond Reservoir Hill, taken by Lida with long tube and squeeze bulb. Left to right: Joie; Sallie Bright; Maude; Zoe; Helen Koehler, from Cincinnati (Robert Koehler's daughter); Lida; Miss McKillip.

PAGE 68.
"Heigho for the Wedding," scene from a play dated Dec. 9, 1891. Left to right, standing: Miss Cravens; Agnes; Tot Barnard (Powell). Seated: Bertie Swope; Amy Graham (Rogers); Agnes Mullen.

PAGE 70.
Flood on the Ohio River, 1882. Robert is at right.

PAGE 72.
Hampton's picnic on Cedar Creek, taken by Lida with long tube and squeeze bulb. Left to right, standing: Ella Hampton (with telescope); Mr. Ketchem; Mrs. Bowman; Maude. Seated: Lida; Jennie Stringfellow; Mary Hampton; Miss Cochran, from Louisville; Zoe.

PAGE 74.
Party at Cedar Cliff, 1892.

PAGE 76.
"Big Creek," 1892.

PAGE 78.
TOP PICTURE. Clifty Falls. BOTTOM. Clifty Creek.

PAGE 80.
Last photograph of Dr. Hutchings, around 1900.

PAGE 83.
Matilda's grandfather, John Henry Ludeling, died in the early 1820's; his wife remarried and lived in Madison, where she died in the Asiatic cholera epidemic of 1849.

PAGE 85.
PICTURE AT RIGHT. The four Koehler daughters. Standing: Mary Van Pelt (1837–1865). Seated, left: Matilda (1840–1914); seated, right: Aurora (1846–1928). Front: Septima Vespasia (1848–1918). There were also three sons.

PAGES 86–87.
In the later decades, Aurora and Septima were already active in missionary schools among the Sioux in South Dakota.

PAGE 96.
TOP PICTURE. John C. Zulauf's report on settlement, the Fischli Papers, is filed with the Indiana Historical Society at Indianapolis.

PAGE 97.
TOP PICTURE. Engagement tea-party at the Hutchings home. Left to right: Mary Hampton (maid of honor at the wedding); Agnes, pouring; Sallie Read of Jeffersonville, who introduced John Zulauf to Agnes; and two friends.

PAGE 102.
"Excuse Us." Amy Graham (Rogers) and Agnes, 1890.

PAGE 103.
TOP PICTURE. "Neighborhood Sketches" from the Louisville Times, Jan. 24, 1939, by kind permission of the artist.
BOTTOM. Concerning Lida: Matilda and her second daughter, Josephine, suffered from bronchitis that became chronic with the years; and around 1910, my grandmother and the maiden aunts began to spend their winters in the high dry climate of Pinebluff, North Carolina. As automobiles became common, Lida drove the sturdy Ford, equipped with Maude's ingenious contrivances for camping out, back and forth across the mountains, even after the others gave up the arduous journey.

In 1938 she finally dismantled the big house, moving everything she could not use into the attic, and arranged the doctor's office as living quarters. Four years later—alone now—she sold the big house for $4,000, piling the contents into the smaller building, as we found it more than 20 years later. That was during the war—and the vast rooms, each opening onto the broad galleries at the side, made excellent apartments for the many newcomers employed at the proving grounds in nearby Charleston. The interior was defaced, but the building itself stood strong and true when it was sold again to the King's Daughters' Hospital across the way. Finding reconstruction impractical, the hospital tore the house down and converted the space into a parking lot.

PAGE 105.
Photograph of the Indiana pioneer home is by W. G. Heberhart. The anonymous poem is from the back of the photo.

PAGE 115.
TOP PICTURE. Southern Indiana farm country: "Looking up Canaan Road from the Mofett place on the hill beyond the glue factory, Oct. 1893."

PAGE 119.
BOTTOM PICTURE. "Anna Friedly with her buggy, horse and dog." Mid-1890's.

FINAL NOTES

The author, only survivor of the Hutchings line, is the granddaughter of Dr. William Davies and Matilda Christine Hutchings and the daughter of Agnes Matilda Hutchings and John C. Zulauf, late President of the Citizens National Bank and Trust Company of Jeffersonville, Ind. In 1917, the Zulauf family moved to New York and later established residence in Europe, where the author studied singing with the famous mezzo-soprano Sigrid Onegin. In Italy, she met and married Pál Kelemen, Hungarian archaeologist and art historian. As war clouds were gathering, they moved to the United States, primarily to pursue his research in the art of pre-Columbian and Spanish colonial America, in which he pioneered. They now make their home in Winter Park, Florida, and Norfolk, Connecticut.

This book is written for the benefit of the Memorial Museum established in the former office and dispensary of the author's grandfather. The Museum has been reconstituted by Historic Madison, Inc., with the help of the interested community. The Riverview Garden Club planted a border of flowers and put in a plot of medicinal herbs. The Jefferson-Switzerland County Medical Society furnished funds for hostesses on given days. A number of friends have made pertinent gifts dating within the period of Dr. Hutchings's occupancy (1882–1903); it is hoped that others will follow suit.

Credit for the realization of the Museum should go first to my aunt Lida Hutchings, last of the Hutchings daughters, who, after the "big house" was dismantled, transferred the contents to the "office" with painstaking exactness. Her loyalty to family memorabilia explains why so many objects were not only saved but also equipped with explanatory labels. She preserved many family traditions, both in writing and by word of mouth.

Next should be named John T. Windle, President of Historic Madison, Inc., who got in touch with us when we opened the house, which had been closed for many years. His connoisseurship of even the smallest details of that period and his energy have made the Museum what it is today, together with the number of historic houses which he has already opened to the public.

Thanks should go also to Ella Hampton of Milton, Ky., close friend of the family, and to Bess Garber, Rachael Haigh and Dana Vail of Madison, who, with their wide knowledge of Madison's past, were helpful in contributing information about family and town history.

Judith Woracek Barry designed this book and carried it through the press. Her husband, Thomas D. Barry, acted as editor and reader of the proofs. Both applied expert knowledge to their tasks and gave the project enthusiastic attention beyond the call of duty.

The Editors of the Journal of the Indiana State Medical Society kindly allowed the use of material from the author's article, "A Horse-and-Buggy Doctor in Hoosierland," published in their July, 1971, volume 64, No. 7. Walter H. Kiser of New Albany, Ind., gave permission to present his Neighborhood Sketch of the Hutchings house (illustration on page 103) as well as pertinent information used on page 3.

My husband, Pál Kelemen, was of great assistance in the culling of the material—not only of the many objects left in the Madison house, but also of the many facts from letters, notes etc. which had to be sorted and evaluated. His unerring eye was invaluable in the selection of photographs from the dozens of albums and family souvenir collections and in their attractive arrangement. Among these were found the pen drawings used on the end papers—the work of my great-uncle, Herman C. Koehler (1835–1916).

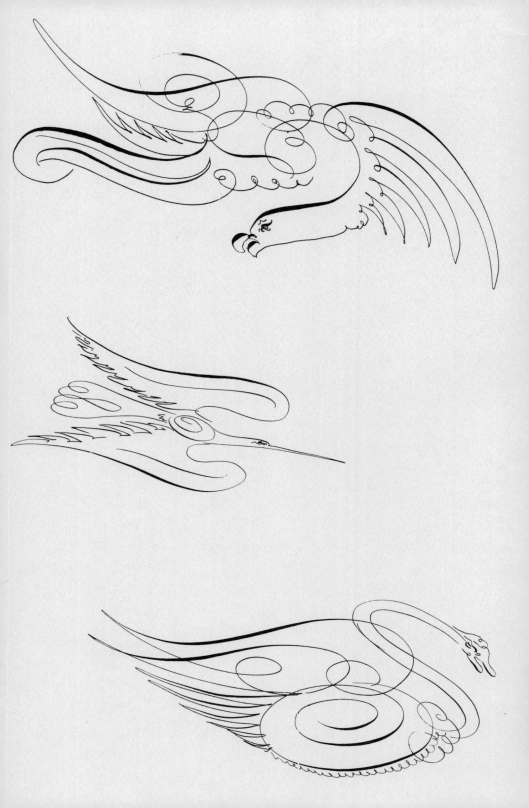